CARTOONS
Bar 2
Pierre Vedel

STUNTS AND BURN-UPS
Ivan Magot
Eric Maurice
Micou
Bertrand Sebileau
Reynald Lecerf
Bruno Gillet
Pierre Vedel
Muzo
Bar2
Jacques Levasseur

SPECIAL THANKS
André Franquin
Barry Sheene
Michel Angélini

TRANSLATION
Philippe Guenet
Neil Murray
Y2K Translation

Comics World Ltd
62 Trade Tower
Plantation Wharf
London SW11 3UF
www.comicsworld.co.uk

© 1990 Editions Vents d'Ouest
Registered: Ocotber 1990
© 2002 Translation Comics World Ltd
Published by Comics World Ltd
ISBN: 0-9543166-0-6

Printed in France
By *Partenaires-Livres®/jl*
Printing completed: August 2002

THE BURN-UP

WELL, I ENJOYED THAT LITTLE THRASH!

YEAH! NICE ONE!

ONE HELLUVA RUN, THAT!

HA! CALL THAT A THRASH?

LOOK, IT WAS ME WHO SHOWED YOU ALL THE RACING LINE!

OH YEAH SURE! AND YOU CERTAINLY USED ALL THE TRACK...

HE DID... INCLUDING THE RUN-OFF AND THE TREES!

THAT WASN'T GOING FOR IT, THAT WASN'T!

YOU CAN TALK, YOU WERE COMPLETELY CROSSED UP!!

NONSENSE. THAT WAS JUST PURE REAR-WHEEL STEERING!

DON'T MAKE ME LAUGH! SO HOW COME I NAILED YOU AT THE CHICANE THEN?

I WAS JUST DAWDLING, REALLY....

CLIK

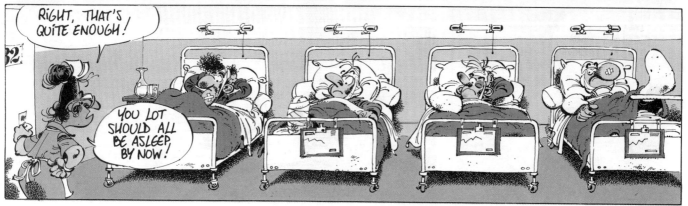

RIGHT, THAT'S QUITE ENOUGH!

YOU LOT SHOULD ALL BE ASLEEP BY NOW!

"BRRRR..... IT'S SUDDENLY TURNED COLD!"

"HEY, HERE'S MIKE!"

"WHAT THE HELL ARE YOU DOING ON THAT HEAP?"

"THAT? IT'S AN OLD NAIL BELONGING TO SOME LOONEY MATE WHO KEEPS INVENTING BLOODY SILLY BIKE GADGETS ...."

"HE'S NEVER GOT THE TIME TO TEST THEM, SO I HELP HIM OUT..."

"KEEPS HIM HAPPY!"

"THIS TIME HE'S KNOCKED UP SOME SYSTEM TO HEAT THE HANDLEBAR GRIPS TO KEEP THE HANDS WARM, Y' KNOW?"

"BUT HIS GADGETS DON'T ALWAYS WORK...."

WOF?

"THIS ONE DOES!"

COME ON, STROKER ....

THIS TIME YOU'RE GONNA BREAK ....

AH! HERE'S WHERE I DROP IT!

... THE LAP RECORD!

VLANG

AS FOR YOUR STATEMENT, I CAN'T UNDERSTAND A WORD OF IT! ...

... FROM THE TOP: " I WAS IN MY FIRST QUALIFYING LAP, I HAD THE RIGHT LINE ON THE POST OFFICE LEFT-HANDER BUT RAN WIDE BECAUSE OF AN OIL SLICK ON THE APEX THAT WAS NOT SIGNALLED BY WARNING FLAGS. ON THE EXIT A BACKMARKER WAS BANG ON THE RACING LINE. WHEN I WENT TO SQUEEZE PAST HIM BY THE KERB HE SUDDENLY DECIDED TO TURN IN FOR A PIT STOP. THERE WAS NO WAY I COULD AVOID THIS NOVICE RIDER ..."

IT'S COMPLETE GIBBERISH!

MANIAC!

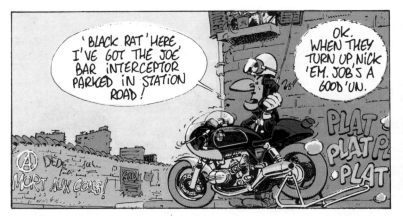

10 MILES ON RESERVE ALREADY AND 20 MILES TO THE NEXT PETROL STATION!

OH WELL! 70 MAX TO EKE OUT THE PETROL. MAKES A CHANGE TO GO SLOWLY...

AND THE OTHERS AREN'T HERE TO TAKE THE PISS!

AND NO WORRIES ABOUT SPEED TRAPS EITHER...!

WHAT A LAFF! EVEN AT THIS SPEED I OVERTAKE SOME PEOPLE!

I DON'T BELIEVE IT!

WELL, WELL... SOMETIMES IT'S NOT SO BAD TO BIMBLE ALONG!...

NO ACHING NECK... THE TIME TO THINK!...

ENJOY THE SUNSHINE... THE SOUND OF THE ENGINE!...

THE PETROL STATION CAN'T BE FAR NOW!...

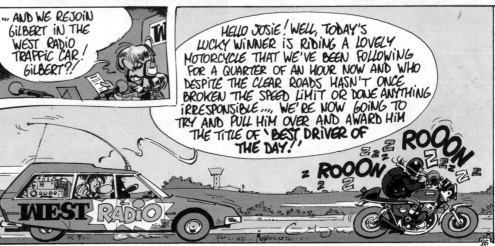

...AND WE REJOIN GILBERT IN THE WEST RADIO TRAFFIC CAR! GILBERT?!

HELLO JOSIE! WELL, TODAY'S LUCKY WINNER IS RIDING A LOVELY MOTORCYCLE THAT WE'VE BEEN FOLLOWING FOR A QUARTER OF AN HOUR NOW AND WHO DESPITE THE CLEAR ROADS HASN'T ONCE BROKEN THE SPEED LIMIT OR DONE ANYTHING IRRESPONSIBLE... WE'RE NOW GOING TO TRY AND PULL HIM OVER AND AWARD HIM THE TITLE OF 'BEST DRIVER OF THE DAY!'

WEST RADIO

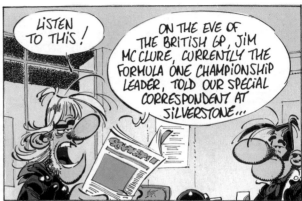

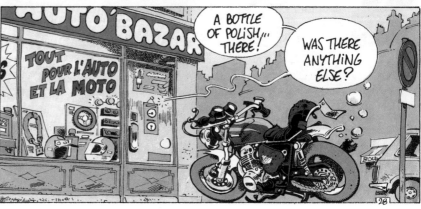

* LIGHTING UP THE REAR TYRE, DRAG STRIP FASHION

JOE BAR TEAM PRESENTS: **STROKER THE RACER!**

I'LL BURY THE LOT OF 'EM!

BLOODY HELL! HALF AN HOUR LATE ALREADY!

HERE THEY ARE!

GET A MOVE ON!

THIS BERK OVER-SLEPT!

I WAS PUKING ALL NIGHT....

HEY, YOU'D BETTER GET A GRIP IF YOU WANT A CHANCE OF WINNING THIS RACE!

DON'T WORRY, LADS, I'LL HAVE 'EM ALL FOR BREAKFAST!

THE OTHERS AREN'T COMING?

WE'RE MEETING 'EM THERE!

THEY SAID THEY WERE GOING TO ENJOY A GOOD THRASH ON THE WAY!

SO WE WON'T SEE 'EM AT ALL THEN!

I'M SURE WE'RE ON THE RIGHT ROAD NOW!

YEAH, BUT DON'T BEND THE BIKE BEFORE THE RACE BEGINS!

BAH, NOW OR LATER ...

RIGHT, STROKER, ME OLD SON! HERE WE ARE!

12TH HILLCLIMB MESDON LES GAS

PAAAA AAARP!

34

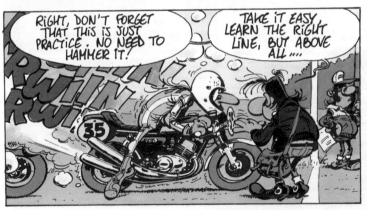

HERE HE IS !

FLAT OUUUT!!

I'M ALIVE! I'M ALIVE!

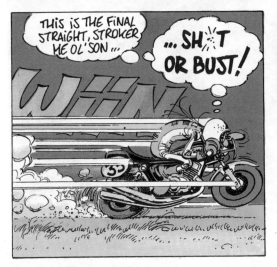

THIS IS THE FINAL STRAIGHT, STROKER ME OL'SON...

...SH*T OR BUST!

DOM

AAARGGGHHH!!

WHA... WHAT HAPPENED ?

YOU WON, STROKER. NOT QUITE AS PLANNED, BUT YOU WON... CALM DOWN. IT'S ALL OVER NOW!

THE BIKE.... HOW'S THE BIKE ?

THE BI... ERRRR...

SORRY, BUT THE RULES SAY THE RIDER MUST CROSS THE LINE WITH HIS BIKE!

...AND WHAT THE HELL DO YOU CALL THAT ?!

I CALL THAT: 'LIGHT FRONTAL DAMAGE'!

HA, HA! VERY FUNNY!

WHEN I SAY: 'WITH HIS BIKE' I MEAN: 'WITH ALL HIS BIKE'!

AND CONSIDER YOURSELF LUCKY I'M NOT ASKING FOR A FULL POST-RACE INSPECTION!

WHAT WAS THAT NOISE?

NUMBER 35 SHATTERING THE LAP RECORD!

35

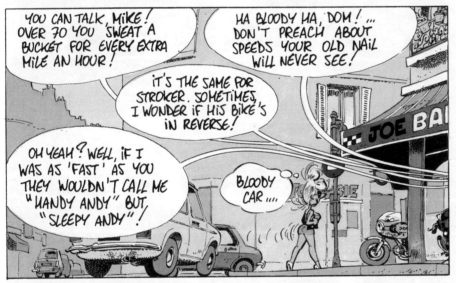

'AVE YOU NOTICED, DEARIE, BUT WITH THESE MODERN BIKES, THE SLOWER THEY ARE, THE MORE NOISE THEY MAKE!

FIRST THING! NO MIRROR!

RAVELIN LE VIEUX

...BUT I SUPPOSE THE SPEEDS YOU DO, YOU DON'T NEED ONE, EH?!

PAH! 'S' BECAUSE IT KNOCKS 2 MPH OFF THE TOP END!

N17

RAVELIN LE VIE

COMEDIAN, EH?

WELL, I LIKE PUTTING DANGEROUS VEHICLES OFF THE ROAD!

N17

RAVELIN LE VIEUX

AND AGAIN!

WHAT'S THIS EXHAUST, EH?

OH, NO, NO, NO, IT'S A SPECIAL DESIGN. ALL STREET LEGAL! HONEST!

STREET LEGAL, EH? LET'S SEE WHAT THE NOISE METER SAYS!

COME ON! START 'ER UP!

@!#*☆*! TYPICAL..... JUST ON THE DAY I'M TRYING OUT A NEW MIXTURE OF 'ROLLING BURN-OUT' AND NITROGLYCERI-METHANOL!

ALL RIGHT, BUT I'D STAND BACK IF I WERE YOU!

NO MESSING ABOUT! I KNOW THE SPECIFIED DISTANCE!

GET A MOVE ON!

BET YOU A FIVER THAT THIS HEAP MAKES MORE NOISE THAN CONCORDE!

BRAQUE

SO WHAT DOES THE NOISE METER SAY?

CRITCH CRITCH!!!!!

39

41

ANGELINI / BAR2 —40

THE BIKES OF THE

NORTON 850 COMMANDO
Andy McCannick on his Mark 1 850 Commando.

Handy Andy's Norton is the 'reliable' version of the 750 Commando which appeared in late 1967. Improved post-1968 by the great engineer-rider Peter Williams, this fabled bike has become a cult object since its launch. Wonderful torque and looks to die for: it will always be associated with rebellious spirits and thrill seekers.

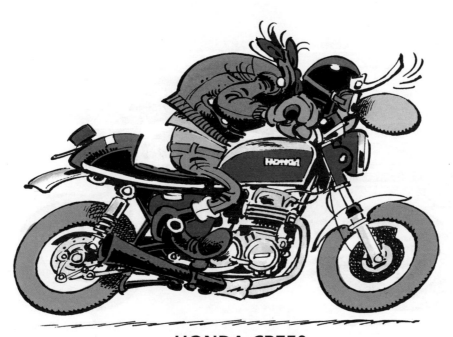

HONDA CB750
Mike Hamschaft hammering his faithful CB750

In 1969, the Honda 750 four introduced the world to four-cylinder motorcycling (a revolution, at the time). Big, impressive, ready to scrape the tarmac with its wide engine, and badly braked despite a factory-fitted disc brake (another revolutionary move for 1969). The Honda Four quickly became a legend despite its faults and contributed to the death of the traditional British bike industry. Note that Mike's machine boasts several typical 1970s mods, such as the aftermarket seat and exhaust.

THE BIKES OF THE

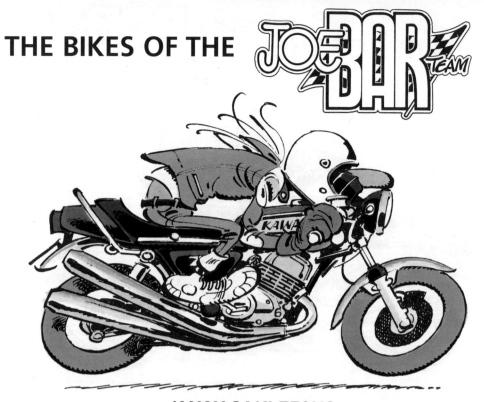

KAWASAKI 750H2

Denis Deljette going for it on his glorious Kawasaki 750 H2.

The magnificient three-cylinder two-stroke screamed into life in 1972. Stroker bought
the green version in 1974. Capable of 125mph and 12 second
standing quarters, the H2 ruled the roads. Torquey, a trifle, um, nervous and with
'interesting' brakes, it understood only one command : 'BANZAI !'

DUCATI 900SS

Dom Esdromico tucked behind the screen of his 900 Ducati.

A dream bike since 1977: a pure race bike for the road. Superb chassis, brilliant hand-
ling, excellent brakes, and powered by a V-twin that won a hatful of trophies, it's THE
bike to complete the Joe Bar Team stable. Phil Read, Paul Smart and the great Mike
Hailwood have all been at the controls of this torquey lean beauty.

IVAN MAGOT